by

Dan & Jason

Simon & Schuster

First published in Great Britain in 2022 by Simon & Schuster UK Ltd

First published in the USA in 2022 by Simon & Schuster Books for Young Readers,
an imprint of Simon & Schuster Children's Publishing Division,
1230 Avenue of the Americas, New York, New York 10020

1 3 5 7 9 10 8 6 4 2

Simon & Schuster UK Ltd
1st Floor, 222 Gray's Inn Road
London
WC1X 8HB

www.simonandschuster.co.uk
www.simonandschuster.com.au
www.simonandschuster.co.in

Simon & Schuster Australia, Sydney
Simon & Schuster India, New Delhi

A CIP catalogue record for this book is available from the British Library.

PB ISBN 978-1-3985-1272-6
eBook ISBN 978-1-3985-1273-3

FSC
www.fsc.org
MIX
Paper from responsible sources
FSC® C020056

GRAB!

PROLOGUE
THE LAST (?) BERZERKER
'm tellin' you... SLURP ...Bill!
She's the ONLY one left.
ZERKS are TOAST!
Not what I heard, Jill!
SQUEAK

I heard she stole something from...
SQUEAK
...the evil WIZARD
WITCH HEAD!

A MAGIC SWORD!
THE SHADOW BLADE!
SQUEAK

Watch where you're waving that drumstick!
It's RUDE!

She says as she chews with her mouth open.
BAH!
That sword is just a legend. Besides, what can one ZERK do?

But that's just IT!
Word is, she's not alone.
SQUEAK

She's recruited...
SQUEAK
...a new band of ZERKS!
SMACK
SLURP
GOBBLE
BLUB
BLUB
BLUB

GLUG
GLUG
GLUG
And guess where they're headed?

HERE!

PWATOOOOOIE
SQUEAK

HERE?!?
Berzerkers are headed to...

CHAPTER 1
MAUG HORN!
THERE! That's the last RAZZLEBERRY SEED planted!
Pat
Pat
Uhhh, PATCHES!

OKAY, RAZZLEBERRY FARMERS!
Prepare to witness the **POWER** of my...
SHOT LAUNCHER!

HA HA HA!
Nice work, FLEMMY!
FWOOH!
Who knew your snot launcher would work so well...
to WATER a new crop of razzleberries!
YAY!
HOORAY!
SNORT!

CHEERS! To a new PARTNERSHIP between HUMANS and MONSTERS!
Glub! Glub!
Snort! Snort!
Uhhh, guys.
Hey.
TAP TAP

This PARTY is...
SWIIIISSH

OVER!
SMASH

SNOT GOBLINS!
Unleash the...
SNOT
On it, Flemmy!

KRAK
BRAK
SNAP
SSSWISH!

THUNK!
ZIP
If anyone else moves, we'll BREAK more than your WEAPONS!

W-w-we're just humble farmers.
We have nothing except delicious berries!

We seek BARB.
Where is she?

BARB?!
We'd never betray BARB!

Talk or FALL.
Your choice, farmer.
DANGER DEEP MUD!
Eeep!
I would fall a thousand times for BARB.
So be it.
DROP!
AH!

SKREEEEEEE SKREEEE SKREEEEE!!!
?
BAT?!? You found Barb?

THUNK!

Huh?

Put him in the wagon with the others.
FWIP
DANGER DEEP MUD!

We're going to...

MAUG HORN!
Hurry, Barb. HURRY.

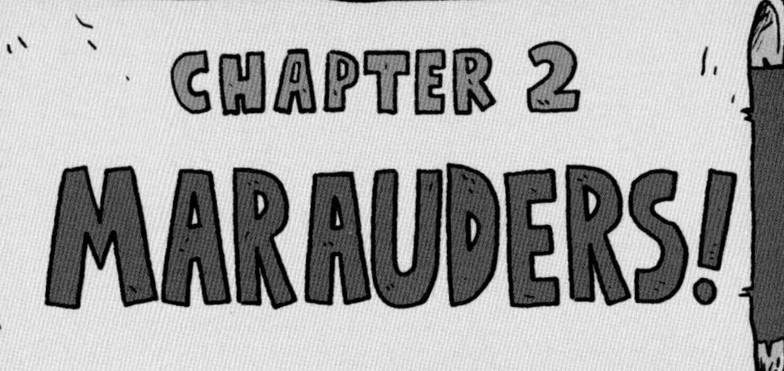

All this walking is killing Grom's feet!

SNORT.

We know, Grom!

You've been telling us about them for the last FIVE HOURS!

SNORT!

PUFF

Actually, PUFF looks like she's PUFF running up that cliff!

PUFF PUFF

Hey! Where's Barb?

Humph.
Huh.
Hup.

We're so close! I can see the gates of MAUG HORN!
Side note: I've started talking to myself again.
BARB!
PUFF
PUFF
PUFF

Yo, P! Check out this amazing view!
Looks great. So, the gang wanted to tell...

P, you okay?
One sec. Air suddenly got thin!
PUFF PUFF PUFF
Er... sure.

Totally FINE.
GASP!
You should really sit down.

PORKCHOP!

Whew!
The gang wanted to tell you we are all a tiny bit tired.
Oh yeah, totally.
Let's take a break.
PUFF
PUFF
PUFF
Perfect. They're already setting up camp!
Grom picked it.

Okay, where?
Just off the road.
He sat down and couldn't get back up.

OUCH!
Grom's feet are killing him!
HEY!
Watch where you're putting those stinky things!
THUMP!
Listen, SWEETIE.
His stinky feet are the least of your problems.

What's that supposed to mean?
And don't call me "SWEETIE"!
Can we please stop talking about Grom's foot odor?
These lands are ruled by a ruthless gang called...
THE MARAUDERS!

They don't scare me!

CRACK!

MARAUDERS!
SNORT?

SNORT!
I knew it was Barb the whole time.
Yo, Zerks. Guess what!
It's not more sausages.
I already guessed that.
BARB!
KRACK!
CRUNCH!
KRAACK!

Even better, I've found a way through these canyons! We'll be in Maug Horn soon!

So now we can sit back and just relax!

AAHH

...HHHH!
SILENCE! Monster scum!
These lands belong to the infamous... MARAUDERS!
Now pay up, or else!

I-I've never heard of you b-b-before!
What?!
And sh-sh-she kn-kn-knows everyone.
Are you sure?
P-p-positive.

It won't matter!
?

These THUGS won't be around for long.
We're... BERZERKERS!
Taking out BULLIES is our JAM!

We are happy to SHARE some of the spoils from these FILTHY monsters!
ZERKS!
BERZERKERS!
W-we've heard of THEM!

HEY!
WHO are you calling FILTHY?!
GROM! Watch the EDGE!

Is this about Grom's FEET?!
KRACK!

CRUMBLE

!
AH!

HANG ON, GROM!!!!
SNORT!
SPLOOP!
STRING SHOT, FIRE!!!
SPLUMP!
I got him!
Snort!
But who's got YOU?!
SNORT!!!

GROM! You okay?

Y-y-yup.

Sooo...these Berzerkers are clowns.

On THREE we all pull him UP!
Side note: P, you have a HUGE spider on your arm.

Ha ha, WHAT?!

SPIDER!

GET IT OFF!!!
AHHHHHHHH

AAHHHHHHHHH!

Everyone okay?
Yup.
Yeah!
SNORT!
Grom says YUP!

What is a Zerk doing hanging around with MONSTERS?!

On second thought, I don't really CARE!

Any last words?
Yeah.

GIVE ME THE POWER!

I AM BERZERKER!
What?!
GROM is going UP!

You dudes stay back! I'll handle these GOONS!
ZAMPH!
THUD!
BARB!

It's raining GIANTS!
!

M
Oh, NUTS!

BATHOOM!

You're SAFE!
Our wagon isn't!
We'd nearly paid it off!

SNORT!
Marauders are escaping!

I'll catch those THUGS!
No, P.
Let 'em go.

We lost this one, Zerks.
It'd be easier if we ALL had magic swords.
SNORT!
Magic swords have their downsides, too.
Try to fix the WAGON.
I gotta sit...
...and REST.

Snort!
GROM! This one goes THERE! THAT one goes THERE!
Uhh... tired.
SSSSSSSSSS

BARB!
SSSSS

BARB!

Wha!

Sweetie, it's ME.

Mom?!
My love, we don't have much time.

You must find Franny Flame Fingers soon!
A battle is coming. And to have any hope of winning...

..you need the Wise Wizards.
Franny Flame Fingers can summon them!
Battle? With who? Witch Head is just one dude.
Not for long. Witch Head has found another portal.
He's going to bring an ARMY to your world.
An army with one purpose...
the destruction of Bailiwick.

Psssst,
Barb.
Uhhh.
Army
coming!

I know I'm
not supposed
to wake a
sleeping...

SHINK!
AAHHH!

Zerk!

Oh, it's
you.

Saved
you some
hamcakes.
Thanks,
P!
Guess I
dozed
off.
How's the
crew?

Grom is sad.
Porkchop messed everything up.
What?!
You kinda did, dude.
You're SCARED of SPIDERS?! Seriously?
SNORT!

They're all legs and eyeballs! EEEEEEEP!

It's not ALL Porkchop's fault!

Dudes, we're Zerks.
We win TOGETHER.
And if we lose...
...we do that together too.

Was your first day as a Zerk as BAD as Porkchop's?
Geez, Kate!

Er, was it?
Okay, gang, story time!
Sweet! Barb's stories are RAD!

My first day as a Zerk!
KRACKLE! POP!

CHAPTER 3
An Unexpected Visit
Who's that?
Sit down, Kate! Let Barb tell it!
SNORT!
THUMP! THUMP!

YAAAWN.

Barb.

Mom!

RUB
RUB
RUB

Open the door!

Yes, Aunt Grackle.

CHUNK
CLACK
CLICK

I didn't hear ALL the locks click!
Sigh.

Tea?
You must use ALL the locks!

Here comes the lecture on monsters.
Must I remind you of all the MONSTERS?!

You're all alone.
I'll never understand why your mother joined up with those Zerks!
SSSSS
Leave room for cream.

I can take care of myself!
My mom showed me rad moves.
Plus, I've been practicing!

With a SHOVEL! HA!

You should use that shovel to dig up mudroot, not fight...
BAM BAM BAM
Who's at the door?
BAM! BAM!
M-M-M-
BAM! BAM
CLICK
CLICK
CLICK
CLICK
CLICK
CLICK
CLICK
CLICK
BAM! BAM! BAM! BAM!
M-M-
KRASH!
MONSTERS!

HA HA HAAAAA!
This sure is easy pickins!!
With no ZERKS around!
Take what you want! Just don't hurt me or the kid!
Barb, THIS is why you lock ALL the locks!
Barb?
Where's Barb?

I'm RIGHT HERE!
Eh?
Huh?
Wha?
You thugs picked the WRONG farm to mess with!

So, what's it gonna be? The easy way?
Or the HARD way?

Uhhh...
Quick question.
Is that a shovel?

Yes, so what?

Heh heh heh heh heh heh heh!
If we pick the easy way...
will you fight us with a GARDEN HOSE?
HA HA HA HA HA HA HA HA HA HA HA HA HA HA HA HA
A garden HOSE! Good one, Lefty!

THUNK

YEEEOOOWEEEEE!

NO MORE...
GAMES...
KID!
YIPES!

SLASH!

You dudes are bullies.
I REALLY don't like bullies.
GRUNT!

BARB!
What are you doing?

I TOLD you.
I'VE BEEN PRACTICING!

KA-KRASH!

CRUNCH
BANG
ZING

SWIISH!
KRAACK!

Kid...
it's...
over.
uh-oh.

KA-
CLANG!

Hi. I'm THUNDER.
A...
B-B-
B-B-
BERZERKER!
You three up for a fair fight?

Eeep!
Yeah, I didn't think so.

You okay, kid?

Yeah, I'm fine!
I'm Barb!
I know.
I've been looking for you.

Looking for me?

I fought with your mom, Raven.

Fought?
I don't understand.

She's gone.
I'm sorry, Barb.

I gotta go, kid.
Wait.
Take me with you. Train me to be a Zerk.
I can't. I promised Raven I'd keep you safe, and this farm is the safest place for you.

Please!
BARB!

Let that fool go and help me fix the door.

Barb?

BARB?

It's unwise to sneak up on a Berzerker.

Stand aside.

I want you to train me to be a Zerk.

This time I'm not taking NO for an answer.

BARB!

I'm sorry.
It's too dangerous for a kid.
Now stand aside.
No.

Listen, dude. I'll make you a deal.
If you can knock ME off into the river, I'll go home.
If I knock YOU off, you train me to become a Zerk.

Very well.
Looks like you could use a bath.

ME?! WHAT?!!

SNIFF!
SNIFF!

Whew.

DOESN'T MATTER!
YOU'RE GOING in the RIVER, dude!
YAAAAAAAAHHHHH!!!

KRACK!

ZIP
DING!
I told you!

THUMP!
I've been...

PRACTICING!
KRAACK!

CRUNCH!
Impressive attacks.

But also...
!
THWUMP!
CARELESS!
Hup!

Enjoy YOUR bath.

SPLOOSH!

Heh heh heh!

Huh?

Barb's cloak.

Where's the rest of her?
Hee hee hee hee!

Time for YOUR bath, dude!
GRAB!
Hurk!

You're kinda heavy.

Nice try, kid!
Hup!

It's over.
Give up.

Fine. I give up.

Look...er...
Barb.
First rule of being a Berzerker: NEVER give up.

Yeah. Got it. But why are you telling me that?
WAIT!
Are you training ME?!
Sure.
Welcome aboard!
YES!
WHOA!

SPLASH!

OOPS!
Thunder, you okay?

SPIT

sniff sniff
I smell better already!

HA HA HA
HA HA HA HA HA HA HA

Thunder! Froglodytes have captured the North Ridge!
?
HA HA! Did this kid knock you into the river?

Uh, yes.
Barb here is a new recruit. She just needs a sword.

A SWORD! So rad!
Nice to meet you.

I'm Boulder.
And thanks for getting Thunder to take a bath!

Boulder, get the others!
We march for the North Ridge at once!

CROAK!
Team, this is Barb. It's her first day on the job!
It's not all fun and games, kid. Sometimes we have to fill out paperwork.
CROAK!
THUNK
THUNK
THUNK
THUNK
CROAK!
CROAK!
THWUMP!

Don't listen to Arrow. There is no paperwork.
CLANG!
CROAK!
CROAK!
Knock off the chitchat, Zerks. We have a job to do.
Barb! Stay BACK and watch how it's done! That's an ORDER!
CROAK!
THUNDER, I GOT THIS!

OUCH, dude!
HOLD STILL!

You're worse than those froggos.

That's why I said stay BACK!

So aside from not listening... how did I do?

That one on your jaw...
is gonna leave a mark.

A reminder of how much I stink as a Zerk.

NO!
It shows how BRAVE you are.

Here, you earned this.

WHOA!

I feel like a real Zerk!

Just remember...
tap tap tap
...a Zerk's TRUE POWER doesn't come from headbands or weapons.
It comes from in here.

Some call it COURAGE!

Others call it HEART!

We Zerks call it...

THE GHOST BLADE!

WHOA!
Coooool.
And also spooky!

Have you ever seen a Ghost Blade? I bet it's awesome! Does it glow?
Well...

the Ghost Blade is more of a metaphor.
It's not real.

Oh yeah.
That makes MORE sense.

But that doesn't make the Ghost Blade any LESS powerful.
Once you find it inside YOURSELF...

you will truly be...
UNBEATABLE!

Whoa.

Find MY OWN Ghost Blade.
Now I gotta grab some Z's.
KRAACK!
PIP!
POP!
Froglodytes have a nasty habit of regenerating at night.

SSSNAP! POP! KRACKLE!
And that, Zerks...

is what YOU ALL must discover inside YOURSELVES!

Any QUESTIONS?

SNORT!
ZZZZ
Grrrrrr.
Weeweeewe
weeweeee.

YAWN!
Meh, that tale does have a few pacing issues.

Yeah, let's catch some Z's.

CHAPTER 4
NO HUMANS ALLOWED!
DUDES! RISE and SHINE!
Today we arrive at...

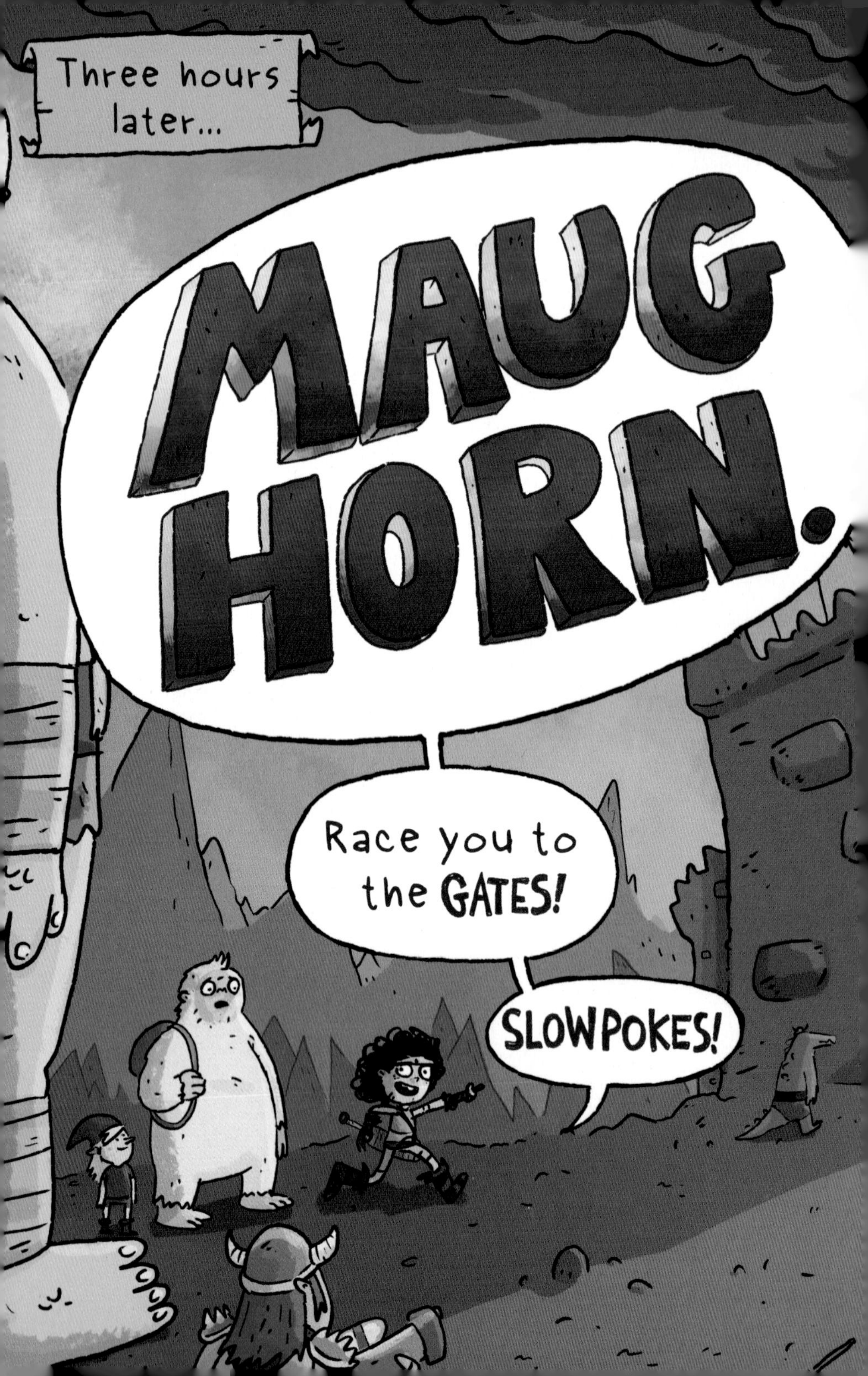

Three hours later...

MAUG HORN.

Race you to the GATES!

SLOWPOKES!

BARB! WAIT!

SLAM!

Not so fast, HUMAN!
?

Doesn't anyone read the SIGN?
NO HUMANS ALLOWED!
Now SCRAM!

Not letting me in just because I'm HUMAN? NOT cool, DUDE!

I said "SCRAM!"

She's not like other humans.
She saved us from the MARAUDERS!
Who?
NO EXCEPTIONS! Now beat it before I lose my temper.

Trust me. It's MY TEMPER you should be worried about.
SHINK
WAIT!
B, there might be another way.
Huh?

P, this is NEVER going to work.
These costumes smell SUPER bad.
Just gimme a sec, B.
I haven't finished adding the FINS!

P! It actually WORKED!

Welcome to MAUG HORN! GREATEST of all MONSTER CITIES!
RAD!

There's the famous MONSTER MARKET!
The Three Towers!
And here is the city center!
What's that AWFUL smell

That's the VOLCANO PIT! It heats the entire city!
With what? FARTS?

I wish we had TIME for sightseeing.
But we HAVE to find Franny Flame Fingers!
TWO teams. Grom, SJ, and Kate.
Porkchop, you're with me.

We meet back here.
By the big smoking pit thing.
BARB!
SNORT!

Be wary of the GUARDS!
If they catch you, the punishment is...
SNORT!
grim.

Good note. Okay, Zerks...
let's get to WORK!

So I know this GREAT BBQ spot. SUPER spicy!
Porkchop! I JUST told everyone we have to...

Hold up.

?

This BELT is so RAD!
It's authentic Daggorn leather.
Twenty dunkets.

Oh yeah...
I'm broke.

Fifteen dunkets! FINAL OFFER!
No. Seriously! I'm OUT of dunkets.
10!
5!

3!
1!
It's not a bargaining trick! I have ZILCH in my pouch! See!

BAH!
Lousy fish heads!

AW.

Porkchop?

Hey, I got you something!

The super rad belt!

Soooo coooooool!
Thank you!
You totally did NOT need to BUY this for me!

You're very welcome!
And I DIDN'T buy it!

Wha?
Did that dude GIVE it to you?

Nope!
I STOLE it!

STOLE IT!
PORKCHOP!

You have to take it BACK!
But...
...don't you LIKE it?

What?! YES! But you don't steal! It's WRONG!

These dudes don't have much.

I'm broke, too!

P. I know.
But we're ZERKS.

We're supposed to HELP.
Not HURT.

Okay.
Afraid of spiders.
Theft.

Some Zerk I've turned out to be.

Hey, P!

?
Uhhh... You dropped this.
Let's go check out that BBQ SPOT!

DROPPED IT?! ME?! THIEF! GUARDS! GUARDS! GUARDS!
Yeah! Great idea, B.
Let's HURRY!

Thief? WHERE?
The YETI and the fish head! They're GETTING AWAY!

Happy now? I did the RIGHT thing!
And NOW they want to throw us in JAIL!
P! The lesson here is DON'T STEAL!

They went this way!
I'm sure of it!
Heh heh, this is kinda fun!

C'mon, I know a shortcut.

THE TWO-HEADED TROLL
This is the place? Looks like a total DUMP!
Trust me. What they lack in cleanliness, they more than make up for in SPICINESS!

BY MY GILLS, PORKCHOP! Come to finally pay your tab?
GLUB GLUB.
HA! Just wanted to show my friend here the BEST BBQ in Maug!

Nice to see a fellow fish head.
GLUB. GLUB.
Seems your choice in company has improved.

Two orders of the SPICY bat wings, please!
On your tab?
Yup.

Er...say, dude, ever see a HUMAN named Franny Flame Fingers?
Er, GLUB. GLUB.

HUMAN? GLUB
NO humans in Maug, not even the dreaded ZERKS dare come here. GLUB. GLUB
SSSSS
SSSS
SEVEN times the Berzerkers tried to take the city. SEVEN times they were turned BACK. GLUB. GLUB.

By our captain of the guards, the LIZARD KNIGHT! GLUB. GLUB.
?!
The greatest DEFENDER of Maug Horn ever. GLUB. GLUB.

Sooooo... that's a NO on Franny.
But a YES to spicy BBQ!
KRUNCH
Hmmmm, we'll see about that!
CHOMP

Seriously, no heat at ALL.
Give it a sec.
I need WATER.

You really think this is haaaaa...

AHHHH

GLUG!

Okay, that's got some HEAT.

Hee hee hee! You folks like FIRE?
GLUB GLUB
Stick around for the show.

Thanks, but we really have to be going.
Maaaah tongue fweeelsh frunny.

MONSTERS old and young... BEHOLD!
It's about to BEGIN!
GLUB GLUB

Give it up for the MARVELOUS MS. MAELSTROM!
Porkchop! Check out her TATTOO!
W.W. The Wise Wizards!
FRANNY FLAME FINGERS

CHAPTER 5
THE DOORWAY

Finally, you've all arrived!
RUB
RUB
RUB
RUB

FIEND!
Barb will stop you!

CLICK
You're right.

Barb is turning into a real pain in my neck.

I'm going to need more than the Shadow Blade alone to defeat her.

GASP!

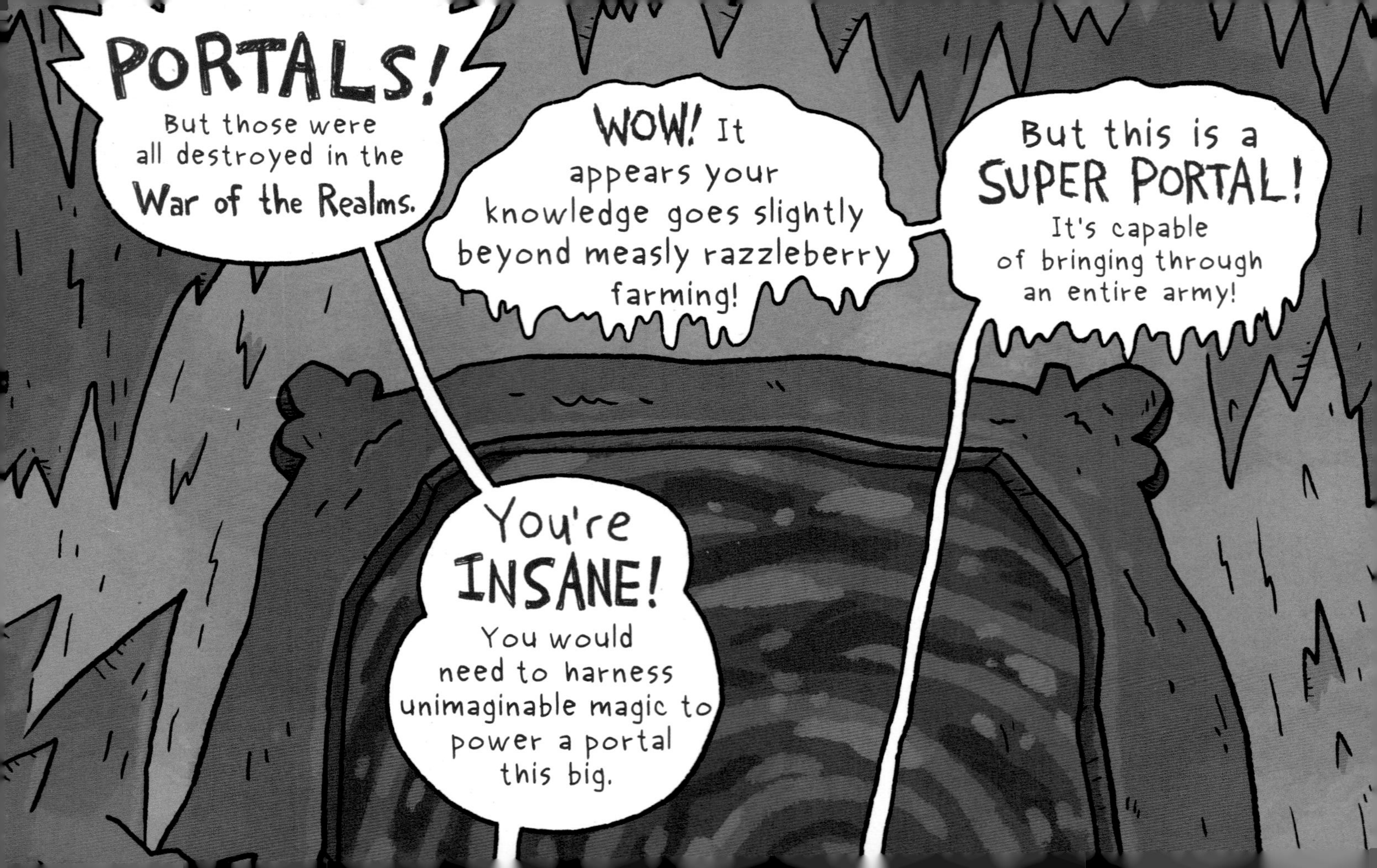

PORTALS! But those were all destroyed in the War of the Realms.
WOW! It appears your knowledge goes slightly beyond measly razzleberry farming!
But this is a SUPER PORTAL! It's capable of bringing through an entire army!
You're INSANE! You would need to harness unimaginable magic to power a portal this big.

OR the power of the Shadow Blade! MUAHAHAHAHA!

NOW DIG.

CHAPTER 6
THE CAGE
CLAP!
You've been entertained!
CLAP!
Maelstrom out!!!
CLAP!
CLAP!
BRAVO!
WOO-HOO!
YAY!

Thank you!
Thank you!
Thank you!
CLAP!
CLAP!
CLAP!

Isn't she GREAT? Bet you two are glad you...

stuck around?
GLUB GLUB

Sigh.

FRANNY FLAME FINGERS!
I knew it.
EEP!

On second thought. Who cares? Yeah, I'm Franny Flame Fingers.
Franny, we need your HELP!
The whole world does.

Whatever. First I gotta get these BOOTS off!
P.U.
P!

On three. Ready? THREE!
Okay.

Whoop!
POP!

WUP!

OOF!

I got the, er, boot.

She's no monster! She's a hu-hu...

...HUMAN!
AHHHHHHHHHH!
GLUB! GLUB!
Oh no.

GUARDS!
GUARDS!

CLINK
Secure the BBQ joint.
CLINK
Yes, sir, Lizard Knight.
TROL

HUMANS! COME OUT WITH YOUR HANDS UP!
P, we have a problem.
Think this is something that creepy sword can fix?

This place is packed.
If I ZERK OUT now, innocent bystanders could get HURT!
I'm giving MYSELF up.

No! Barb, you can't!

GO! You're a MONSTER. You can blend in!
Take the SWORD and find the OTHERS!

Now GO!
That's an order.

TROLL
Hey, GUARDS, today is your LUCKY day.

You get to meet a real live BERZERKER!

KA CHUNK

Great.
PA-TOOF!
This is total overkill, dude.
THUMP!

Know this, BERZERKER.
When it comes to protecting MY city,
I don't take any chances.
Except with FOOTWEAR!
Those BOOTS are very DARING.

ZERKS never work alone.
Where are the REST?
DUDE, I work solo.

Perhaps the CAGE will teach you to TELL the truth.
Guards, take her away.
Sounds lovely.

How come you guys don't have COOL BOOTS?
Quiet, ZERK!
I'D like some cool boots.

C'mon, they just put fresh meat in the CAGE!
Ooooooo! Here's a squishy one!

HURRY! Let's go!
I'm hurrying! I'm hurrying!

That cage!
HUP!

Humans are GROSS!
SPURP!
Hungry, human?!
SQUASH!
HA! HA!
SPLOP!
Don't you kids have school?

DANG, that kid has an...

SPLAT
arm.

KATE! SLIME JAW!
GROM!
Crikey! You'd think a GIANT would be easier to find!

Watch it, yeti!
THUD!
AHHH!

THUMP
Ow.

Grom says no!

Grom thinks you are the special fire wizard.
Nah, bro, I'm a fire giant. Totally different.
Sooo... Grom is half right?
SNORT
Told you, Grom!
ARGH! We're getting nowhere!!!
KATE!
PUFF! PUFF!

Porkchop? Wait, where's BARB?

The guards got her!
OH NO!
She'll be in the CAGES for sure!

We need to break her out!
SNORT
LET'S GO!

NO HUMANS ALLOWED
Hey.

ALLOWED
Lizard Knight caught a Zerk. Keep an eye out.
Hmph.

ALLOWED
Tell the Lizard Knight not to worry.
No one is getting in without my say-so!

I am.
Uhhhh...no. No humans allowed. Doesn't anyone read the sign?
You really think a sign...

is going to stop...
You're really scary.

ME?
!
Wha!

I'm a member of the GREEN GUARD!
Sworn DEFENDER of Maug Horn!

Take me to the ZERK.
NOW!

NO HUMANS AL ED
You know what? This job is overrated.
OW!

CHAPTER 7
ZERK SHOWDOWN
At least this can't get any WORSE.
SPLORT
SPLAT
So BERTHA, we meet again!
Oink!
YES!
Me and my big mouth.
Good one!
HA! HA!
HA! HA!
HA!

Okay!
Ready?

THUD!

AHHGH!
OUCH!
Huh?

Outta the way, runt!
HEY!
THONK!

Not cool, dude!
They're just kids!
If you feel like a fair fight, I'm right here!
OUCH!
OOF!

WAIT?!
THUNDER?!
What happened to you?
Witch Head made me into something...
BETTER.

Better?
Went a little heavy on the goth thing if you ask me.

Is it the shoulder spikes AND the wrist spikes?
Never mind that...

Where is the...
SHADOW BLADE?!!

I'll **NEVER** tell!
And **YES!** Way too many spikes!

Very well.
Talk— or the kid falls.

NO!
AHHHH!

Hey! MEET...
Huh?

FOE SQUASHER!

GROM!
The name of that thing is growing on me!

Hey, B! We'll get you out!

Boy, am I glad to see you!

SNORT
BARB, STAND BACK!
I'll use some ACID PHLEGM on those bars.
KACHUNK

ZINNG!
KRASH

ZIP
THUNK

Grom says huh?
?

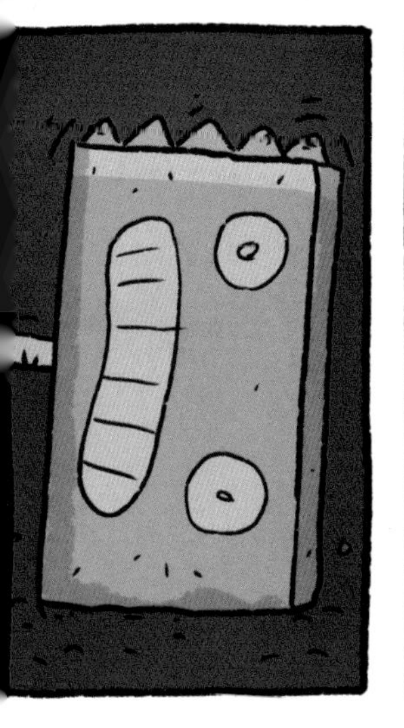

GRAAH!

Giant,
meet...

THE SHADOW REAPERS!

Uh-
oh.
Sooooo, the yeti has the SHADOW BLADE!
Get it.

CLINK!
CLINK!

CLINK!
CLINK!

CAPTAIN!
BANG!
What is it now, Sergeant?

SHADOW REAPERS, inside the gates!

...
Show me.

SLASH!
Grom says... AHH!
Grom!

SHWIP!
SHWIP!

Kate!
YIPE! STUCK!
SPLAT!

It's over, yeti.
THUD!

The SWORD, NOW!
BARB!

Airmail! GAH!
THOOOM!
Huh?

THUNK

Okay, REAPS,
Let's ROCK AND ROLL!

Give me the POWER!

I AM BERZERKER!

KAKOOM!
THWAM!!
THOOM
CRACK!

KAZUNK!
OOOOOOM!

That's ALL of the Reaps.
All except...

One.

Your powers are impressive.

But they won't last much LONGER.

Use them to STOP me.

AAAA

Or SAVE him.

NO!
AHHHHH

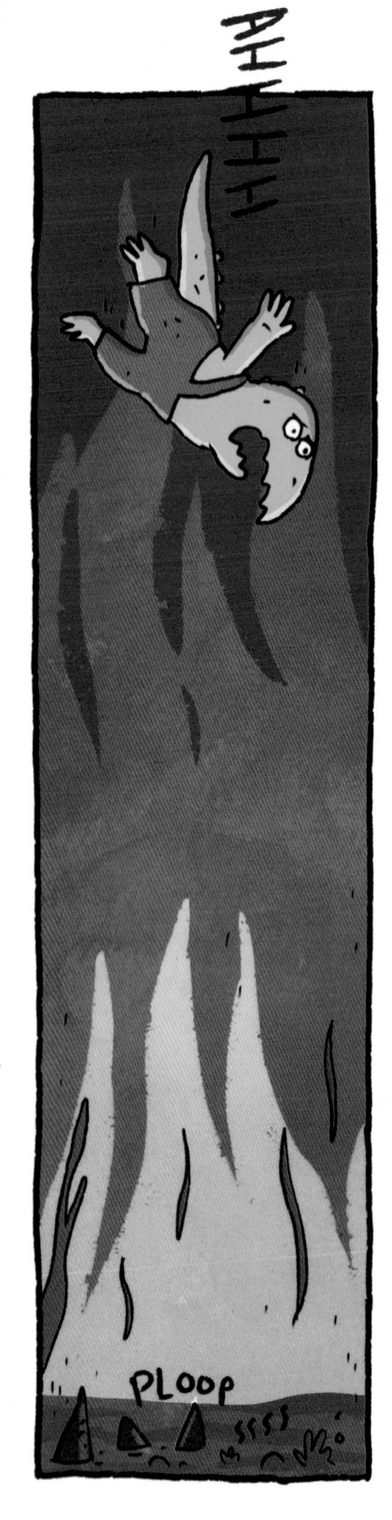
AHHHH
PLOOP
SSSS

AAAAAHHHHHHH
ploop
SSSS
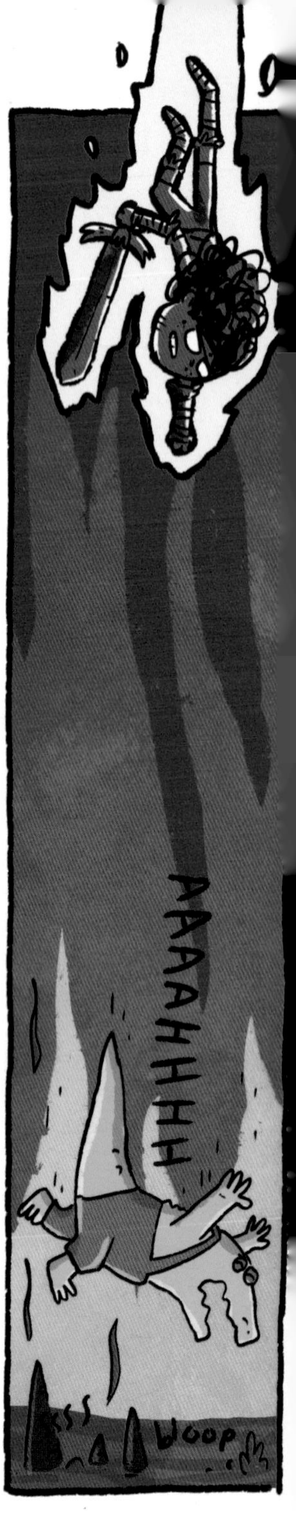
AAAAHHHHH
SSS
WOOP

I GOTCHA, KID!
SSSSS
BLOOP
PLOOP!

The Shadow Reapers!
Hold up.

Why are they staring into the pit?

You're out, kid! cough. cough.
Huff! Huff!

So, Spiky Reaper...
Shadow Reaper.
Sure. I was thinking...
Lemme go...
Cough!
...and we can call it a tie.
You made your CHOICE.
YOINK
It was your last.

DANG! THE DROP is totally your move!
We've loaded the prisoners into the wagons.
All except the yeti known as Porkchop!
He's missing.
No matter. We have what we came for.
We must return to Witch Head.

CHAPTER 8
THE LIZARD KNIGHT
LIZARD KNIGHT!
WHAT ARE YOU DOING?!?!
PPKKSSSSSSSS

So hot.
C-c-can't see.
Mom, if you...
...can hear me.

I'm sorry.

I couldn't save Bailiwick.

CLICK
ZWIP
ZZZZZZZ
piff!
SCHWIP!

I got you, ZERK.
You're safe now.
Thanks.
COUGH!
COUGH!
Never thought I'd be happy to see those boots again.

My whole life has been dedicated to protecting monsters from humans.

But you risked your life for a monster.

You SAVED my son!
Thank you.
Awww, no sweat, dude.

RUMBLE!
CRASH!
CRUNCH!
?
Huh?

SCRRRAPE!
Ow.

Where is everyone?
PORKCHOP!
The Shadow Reapers got them.

NO! What about the sword.
Gone.

Witch Head will get the sword for sure. Then we're all toast.
You're right.

But Witch Head doesn't have it yet.
I say we keep it that way.

Huh? I thought YOU didn't care.

I didn't.
But WOW! Seeing you save that kid!

Barb, you're something really special.
I can help you.
Yeah? A lot of good it's done me.
Excuse me.

Another human? Sheesh.
Follow me. We'll take this someplace more...

SQUEEEEEEEEEEEEEEEEEEEEEEEEEEEEE
private.

THUD!
The dungeons. Always figured I'd end up here.
Creepy.
sniff sniff
Sorry about the smell.
I'll keep watch outside.

Okay, you said you can help. HOW?

I'll contact the others.
Together we can decide how to defeat Witch Head once and for all.

Contact the others.
How?

Fire can do more than BURN.
You two should stand back.

PORKCHOP! Check it! MAGIC!

FIRESIGHT!
HUH? AHHHH!
WHOA!

WENDY WIND WALKER
The winds of change stop for no one.
WALLY WATER WEAVER
Hello from down below!
STU STONE SKULL
What's crackin'?
CARRION CUSTODIAN OF THE CREEP
Ssssup, y'all.
R.I.P.
!
BEHOLD, THE WISE WIZARDS!!!

Franny, what's the deal with the picture quality?
You look fuzzy.
Sorry, I'm a little rusty. It's been a long time since I've used my powers.

Tell us!!!

This kid, with the curly hair. Right here.

Ummm. Really?

You sure?

Hmph!

I don't see it.

Trust me. I've
een it with my own eyes.
She fights for everyone.

Monsters and humans alike!
And they fight for her.

Barb can save BAILIWICK!!!
But she needs the Shadow Blade.

The Shadow Blade is protected by my Stone Bots!

Zerks got tricked into kicking their stony butts.

Rocks! Those took forever to make!!!

Now those Zerks have the sword.

And they have transformed into Shadow Reapers.

Shadow Reapers?

The only way Witch Head could have changed Zerks into Shadow Reapers is with a...
MIND SUCKER!
Heh heh heh heh heh.
YUCK!
I hope not!
Don't mind CARRION!
She made those dreadful things!
Yesss, I made them.
To HELP win the war with th monsters!

My friend Thunder is a Shadow Reaper. Will he be that way FOREVER?

Not THUNDER! I knew him well! Fret not, there is a way to undo the spell.
Make him LAUGH!
?

You mean, like, tell him a joke?

The Mind Sucker obscures your humanity.
Laughter will help Thunder remember.

One good zinger will do it!

Monsters fighting for humans! I gotta see this. I'm in.
If Franny vouches for the kid, then I'm in.
Zerks defeating Stone Bots! WOWZA!!! I'm in!
I can't sit out a good fight! I'm sssSummon ussss
I thought you'd never ask!
Barb, yeti, stand back!
Okay, Franny! FIRE AWAY!
This is so RAD!
Maybe she'll summon some snacks, too!

BEHOLD: THE PORTAL OF FIRE!
SSSSSSSSSSS
Franny, what happened?
That was anticlimactic.

Okay, take two...
Behold: the POWER of the PORTAL of FIRE!
SHOOOOO...
POP!
PUFF!
BWEEEEEEE...Poof.
I-I-I can't do it!
What?!

Franny, what's wrong?!
My powers are...gone!

I can't SUMMON anyone!
It's hopeless!

Can't you just, er...try again?

I quit the war. I quit magic. I went into hiding in Maug Horn to pursue the art of juggling!
It's been so long since I was a real Wizard, my powers don't work anymore.
I can't help you!
Unless it's about juggling.

BOOTS

!
SQUEAK!
THUD!

How was the meeting?

That bad, huh?

CHAPTER 9
DOOM-
SMASHER!

So what now, Barb?
Barb?
Barb?
Barb?
Barb?
Barb?
Barb?
Barb?

It's **OVER,** dude.

I was supposed keep the Shadow Blade **SAFE.**
But I **LOST** it.
I was supposed to **SAVE** Bailiwick.
But I **COULDN'T.**

I thought I could be a **ZERK.**

But... I'm **NOT.**
THUD!

BARB!
You're the most AMAZING human I've ever met.
SQUEEZE!
SQUEEZE!
Whoa! Thanks, P.

To be honest, before I met you...
RUMMAGE! RUMMAGE!
KEEP

I didn't give a fig about anybody!
WIPE WIPE WIPE

You changed all that.
Win or lose,
I believe in you.

?

My hand is... glowing?

So Barb, what's the plan?

Now it's stopped.
Weird.

Hmmm...what would be the fastest way from Maug Horn to Castle Skunkwark?
SAUSAGE!
What's that? Where ya headed?
Grab a sausage before you go!
squeak squeak

SNIFF SNIFF SNIFF

Ha!

What are YOU, of all humans, doing in Maug Horn?
Kielbasa?

I've had a change of heart about monsters.

Barb...you opened my eyes.

Cool, dude!

Plus! They love my sausages here!
It's a whole new market!
But wait!
You mentioned you need to get to Castle Skunkwark!
SA

Yeah. The fastest way would be over those peaks, right?
Aye...the Devil's Backbone. The highest peaks in Bailiwick.
Doesn't look so bad.
SAUSAG

Not bad! Tell me, yeti...
HA HA HA HA HA HA HA HA HA HA HA HA HA HA HA HA HA
SA
under all that hair do you have a pair of wings?

HA HA HA HA HA HA HA HA

Yetis with wings!
Now I remember why I don't like this dude.
Maybe I can help.

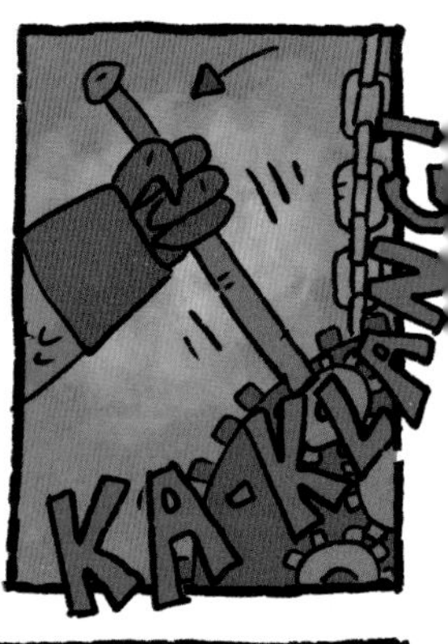
KA-KLANG!

These thugs are serving time for running an illegal fighting pit.
You up for taking these two on the scenic route to Castle Skunkwark?

We'll NEVER help this Zerk!
NEVER!!!
Oink!

Help her, and I'll let you go free.
Oink!

BRENDA! I didn't see you there! More than happy to help!
Huh?

CLICK

P. Look! We've got WINGS!

Oink! Oink! Oink! Oink! Oink! Oink! Oink!
Uhh...Barb, I'm not so sure about this.
One more thing, Barb!

You lost your WEAPON.
It would be an HONOR if you too
one of mine.
Ouch!
THUD!
BEHOLD,
DOOMSMASHER!
This blade has kept Maug Horn SAFE.

May it now keep you SAFE!

This blade is RAD!
THWIP!
The HONOR is mine, dude!!

One last thing...

my BOLT LAUNCHER.
This could prove useful in the mountains.

You are a friend of Maug Horn now.
If you need help, you only have to ask, Barb the Berzerker.
Help!
Please!

CHAPTER 10
THE SPIRE BRIDGE

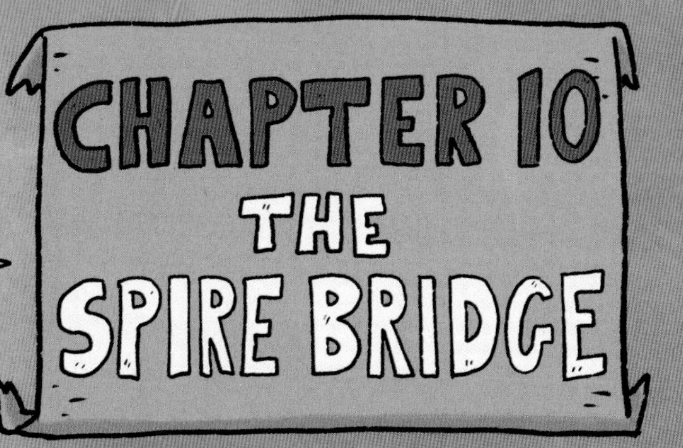

Behold...
THE DEVIL'S BACKBONE!

Wow.
Told ya, P!

So, what's the plan?
What are we gonna do if we catch Thunder and his SHADOW REAPERS?

The Wise Wizards said the Mind Sucker spell is broken by LAUGHTER!

We just have to stay alive long enough to tell them my HYSTERICAL jokes!

But your jokes are so BAD!

WHAT?!? No they're not.

Hate to butt in. But we've got bigger problems than bad jokes!
oink oink
The Spire Bridge is just ahead...
...but so is that...

BLIZZARD!
Trappers! Brace yourselves!
It's about to get...
WINDY!
SWEEEEEEEEEEEEEEEE
WAHHHH

Let us down! You've gotten us close enough!
OKAY!
oink

GOOD LUCK, BERRTHAA!
IT'S BA- never mind.
THANK YOU!
Hey, B!
Uhh, where's the ground?!?

I think I see...
SLAM!
LAND!
OUCH!

TOO STEEP!
SKRIKT!
CAN'T HOLD ON!

GAHH!
CAN'T STOP!

SHUNK

P!

GOTCHA!

Now we just need to climb back up this mountain.

Somehow.

Hey, Barb.
What if...

We go THROUGH the mountain.
WOOOOOOOOEEEEEE.

We don't really have the best luck in caves.
But it's better than freezing our butts off out here!
SNIFF SNIFF
Cave passes the sniff test!
Does that sniff test really work?
YEAH.
It's always right!
Half the time.

Looks like your nose got it right!
The nose knows!
That tunnel leads through the mountain to the Spire Bridge!
Told ya!
We just have to cross these weird stones!

Piece of hamcake!

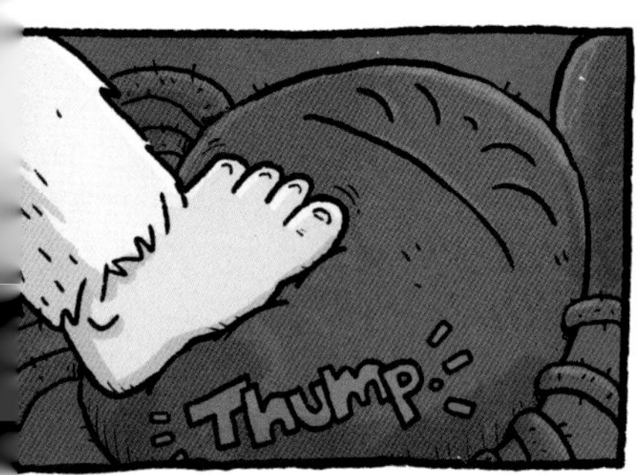
Thump

KRICK

A SP-SP-SPIDER!
Uh, P.

Not A spider.
KRICK
KRICK
KRICK
KRICK
KRICK
KRICK

It's...
SPIDERS!
KRICK KRICK
P-P-PLURAL?!?
We'll never make it through in time!

Plural!
KRICK
KRICK
KRICK
KRICK
BARB!
I have an idea!

Whoa, dude!
What are you doing?
JUST HANG ON, B!
RR!
RRRRRR!

Here goes nothin'!
RRRRR!
RRRRRR!

BAM!
POW!
BIFF!

Porkchop, we're not going to make it!
WE won't.

But YOU will!
Wha?

PORKCHOP!
THERE'S NO TIME!

DON'T WORRY!
POP
I GOT THIS!
SHMUSH!
Now go save Bailiwick.

But these are spiders!
You're terrified of spiders!

They don't scare me anymore.
I found my...
SPOOKY SWORD!

Ghost Blade, P.
It's called... You know what? Doesn't matter.
Porkchop, you're a true ZERK!

Meet me at the SPIRE BRIDGE!
I've got some punch lines to deliver!

CHAPTER 11
SOMETHING STIRS
KLANG

You deluded FOOL! Barb will stop you! When she gets here, YOU'LL be SORRY!

HUK!

Somebody is gonna be sorry, that's for sure.

SKREETCH!!!!

SSSSSSSS!
Well, hello there.

SSSSSSSSS

THE SHADOW REAPERS have the sword and are racing to Castle Skunkwark.

WORK HARDER, YOU FOOLS! THE END IS NIGH!

GASP!

If Barb is on her way, then the end is nigh for you!

No, the end is nigh for you!
No, you!
No, you!
No, you!
No, you!
No, you!

NO, YOU!
NO, YOU!
?

NO, YOU!
NO, YOU!
NO, YOU!
NO, YOU!
NO, YOU!
WITCH HEAD!

What are you up to?
SSSSSSSSSSSSSSSSSSSSSSSSS

CHAPTER 12
THE GHOST BLADE!
Shadow Thunder.
Someone blocks the Spire Bridge.
Not for long.

BERZERKER.
You should have STAYED in the PIT.

Too hot.
But honestly, now I'm a little cold.
I bet kicking your **BUTT** will make me feel warmer.
I used to feel. Witch Head cured me of that weakness.
Okay, last chance, No Funder.
GIVE me the **SWORD.**

For the LAST time.
It's SHADOW THUNDER.
And I am too fun.
No. Not really.
Shadow Arrow...

if you get a shot,
take it.

RRRRRRRR

When I throw you off this bridge,
your body will freeze before it ever hits the ground.

If Witch Head gets the Shadow Blade, dude...
he will unleash an ARMY on this world...
that will turn Bailiwick into a GRAVEYARD.
I'm NOT going to let that happen.
And neither are YOU!

I-I can't help you.
My mind belongs to Witch Head.
I know how to get...

YOU back.
SSSHINK
KAKLANG!
JOKES!

Huh?
Why do ducks have tail feathers?

SWISH!
To cover their BUTT QUACKS!
BUDDA! BOOM! CHING!

GARGH!
Not a fan of duck humor?
Okay. I got others.

What did the centaur say when he walked into the pub?

PUNCHES!
AND...
KICKS!
AND...
EVEN MORE KICKS!

You're toast, dude!
STAY down.
The only way to get your mind back is...
to make you laugh.
So, listen up!
What did the Vampire Goat Fiend order for dinner?

Time to change tactics.
A yeti?
Close!
Anything! Get it—cause they eat...

Yes. Your joke just cracked me up.
You broke the spell.
Eh? But you didn't really laugh.

HAR. HAR. HAR. HAR. HAR!

There. Happy?

Err...okay.

Welcome back, Thunder.

HA!

SLAMM
GAH!
Trusting FOOL!
CHEAP SHOT, dude!

BAM!

KLANG

THOOM!
!

DOOMSMASHER!
Time to GIVE...

UP!
THWAM!
AHHHHH!!!
Uhhhh...
You once...
told me...Zerks...
never do...
that.

Zerk, any last words?
I don't really care.

But Witch Head may find them...
...amusing.
Ugh...I need a vacation.

Wish PORKCHOP was here...

He was totally kicking those spiders' BUTTS.

Don't worry, Barb...I found my spooky sword!

Spooky sword... heh heh.
Hey, it's worth a shot!

Yo, got my last words, dude.
Remember what you told me my first day as a Zerk?

NO! My mind is under Witch Head's control, remember?

Uhhh...
That was kind of a rhetorical question.

Zerks NEVER give up because...
...inside us is what some people call...

COURAGE.
Others call it...

HEART.

But Zerks,

YAAHHRGH!
we call it...

THE GHOST
GAH!

BLADE!

SHAZOOM
?!!

The GHOST BLADE.
It's REAL!

TSSSSS
WHOA!

THUNDER!

GRAB!
Zip!
CLUNK!
DUDE!
YOU GOTTA HELP ME!
YOU'RE SLIPPING!
No.
Let me... GO.

NO!

THUNDER!

GRAB!

Side note:
I thought the **FULL MOON** wasn't until **NEXT** week.
Huh?

GOTCHA!
YOINK!

Heh...heh...heh.
SHOOOOOM
HA HA HA! Stop laughing, Thunder Buns.
I'm gonna DROP you!
HA HA HA HA HO! HO! HO HO!
HA! HA! HA!
HA! HA! HA! HA!

FULL MOON! HAH HAH HAAA!
SHOOOOM!
HA HA HA HA
SHWIP!
Whoops!

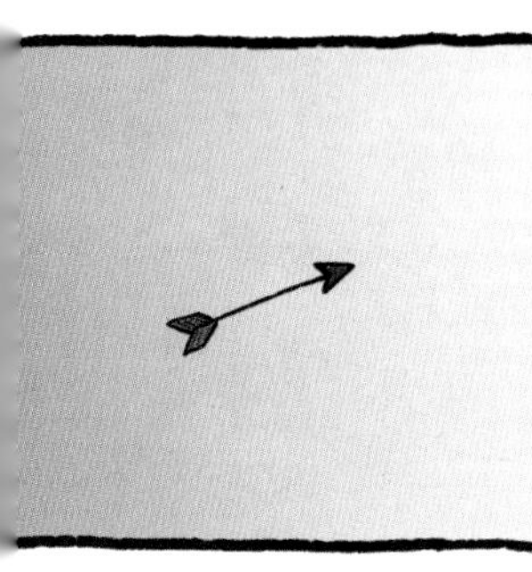

Barb, what happened? My head feels like jelly.

Long story, dude. Let's get you up.

GAH!
THUNK!

BARB!

What's happening to the Shadow Reapers?
Brain feels like mush.

They're **ZERKS!**
snort

It's okay.
You're going to be okay.
Uhhh...
Gently...that's it...there.

BOULDER!
BARB needs help!
SKREEEEEEEEE

No.
SKREEE

SSSSSSS
SSSSSSSSSSSS

The sword Ssss...
NOOOOOOOOOOOOOOOOOOOO!
The Berzerker..
Witch Head will be pleasssSed!

CHAPTER 13
ZERKS VS. ZERKS
UGH, I an't believe I ost Barb to BATS!
I have to get the others....
There's still time to save...

BARB?!
WUNK
WHERE IS SHE?

Wha-
what are
you? Some kind
of tarantula
bigfoot?
Huh?

Oh, this?
This is my cool
new hat.
Actually,
I'm starting to
have second
thoughts.

Well, if you're trying to get to Barb...
you gotta go through...
THUNDER!
SOCK

Fine by me!
HOOAH!
POW
BIFF
WHAP
WHACK
THUD
THUMP
BAM
Oh, jeez.
BWEEEEEEEEEEEEEEEEET!
Huh?
Wha?
Yo, dudes.

While you two were fighting,
we figured out we're all on the same TEAM!
What?
We are?
YES!
NOW,
KNOCK IT OFF!

DUDES, listen up!
Barb is in TROUBLE!
Witch Head has the SHADOW BLADE!
What are WE going to do?

I, AVALANCHE, say we all go and save BARB! Witch Head will soon learn, when you mess with ONE ZERK...

you mess with ALL of us!
Who's with me?
WOO-HOO!
YEAH!
WE'LL SAVE BARB!

Stop.
Don't you want to save Barb?

More than anything.
But Witch Head with the Shadow Blade is...
...unbeatable.
We can't face him alone again.
We need the WISE WIZARDS!

The WISE WIZARDS?
They all VANISHED back to their realms.
We would need a SUMMONER to reach them.
It's impossible.

We found Franny, but...she COULDN'T summon the WIZARDS, much less a few snacks.

Like I said, impossible.

There is ANOTHER way.

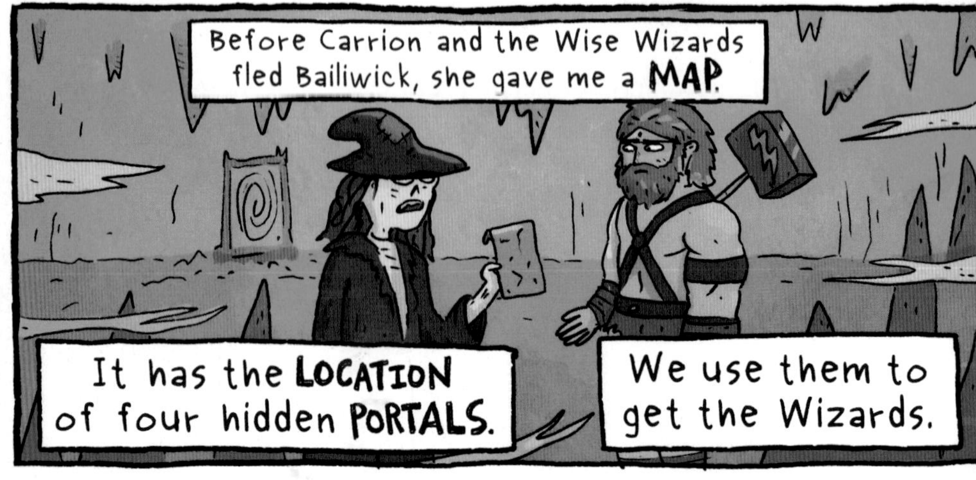
Before Carrion and the Wise Wizards fled Bailiwick, she gave me a MAP.
It has the LOCATION of four hidden PORTALS.
We use them to get the Wizards.

ARROW
FROSTBITE
You find Wendy Wind Walker.
KATE
ICEBERG
SLIME JAW
Portal to Zephyr
GROM
Go get Franny Flame Fingers.
You find Wally Water Weaver.
BOULDER
AVALANCHE
THE TWO-HEADED TROLL
Portal to Turtle Deep
Portal to Grindor
You find Stu Stone Skull.
CLAYMORE
YETI
It's Porkchop!
STEVEN
You find Carrion Custodian of the Creep.
Portal to the Creep
Meet at Castle SKUNKWARK with your WIZARD.
Then the REAL FUN begins.

!
Here, kid. Take my headband. It's yours.
Don't worry. It's adjustable
WHOA...dude.
But I thought you were coming with us?
I once PROMISED a Zerk, if anything happened to her, I'd keep her daughter SAFE.
I intend to KEEP that promise.

Wait a sec! He's talkin' about BARB! He's goin' after BARB!
Yup!

HEY!
Huh?
Yeti, hinder me at your own PERIL.

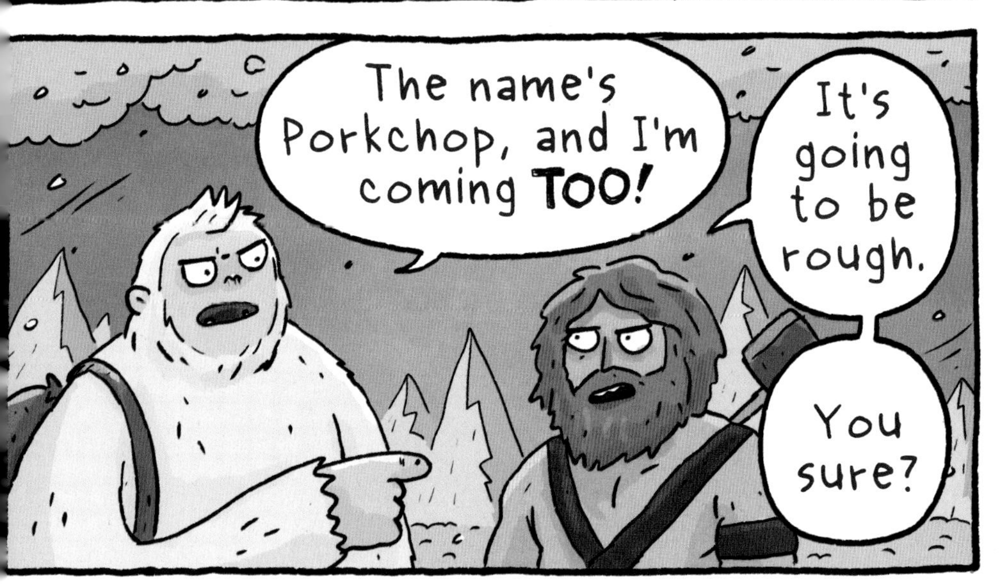
The name's Porkchop, and I'm coming TOO!
It's going to be rough.
You sure?

YES, I'm sure!
Barb helped me find my...
?
SPOOKY SWORD!
So now I'm totally UNBEATABLE.
Er, you mean the Ghost Blade?

NO!
SPOOKY SWORD!
GHOST BLADE!
SPOOKY!
GHOST!

SPOOKY!
GHOST!
SPOOKY!
GHOST!
SPOOKY!

HEY!

Seriously? You're about to face certain DEATH and you're fighting over semantics?!!

Eh?

Let's settle this **AFTER** we kick Witch Head's **BUTT!**
And SAVE **BARB!**

Agreed, PORKCHOP!
Spoken like a true...
BERZERKER!

SKREEEEEE!!!
Heh. Heh.
Ouch.
Hurts to laugh. But DANG! Full moon! Ha! Ha!
Ouch.
And Porkchop doesn't think I'm funny!

HA HA
HA
HA HA HA HA
HA HA HA
HA
HA
HA
HA
To be continued...
Wait...WHAT! Barb is laughing In MY moment of triumph?! So rude!

Dan and Jason are a two-headed troll that grew up in Vermont. As a little two-headed troll they enjoyed smashing toys together, drawing comics, and joking around about stories and stuff. They were best pals back then and they are best pals today. Now fully grown, they still enjoy drawing comics and joking around although they don't smash their toys together...as much.

Dan and Jason are the creators of the Barb the Brave series! Be sure to check out the first book, as well as their hot wings tavern in Maug Horn!